SACRED LOVE

£2·99

This publication is not authorised for sale
in the United States of America and / or Canada

Magnetic Publishing Limited/
EMI Music Publishing Limited

Published by:
EMI Publishing Limited / Magnetic Publishing Limited.

Exclusive distributors:
Music Sales Limited
Distribution Centre, Newmarket Road,
Bury St Edmunds, Suffolk IP33 3YB, England.
Music Sales Pty Limited
120 Rothschild Avenue, Rosebery, NSW 2018, Australia.

Order No. AM979187
ISBN 1-84449-340-7
This book © Copyright 2003 by
EMI Publishing Limited / Magnetic Publishing Limited.

Unauthorised reproduction of any part of this publication by
any means including photocopying is an infringement of copyright.

Music arrangements by Jack Long.
Music processed by Paul Ewers Music Design.

Printed in the United Kingdom by Caligraving Limited, Thetford, Norfolk.

www.musicsales.com

Your Guarantee of Quality:

As publishers, we strive to produce every book
to the highest commercial standards.

While endeavouring to retain the original running order of the
recorded album, the book has been carefully designed to minimise
awkward page turns and to make playing from it a real pleasure.

Particular care has been given to specifying
acid-free, neutral-sized paper made from pulps which
have not been elemental chlorine bleached.

This pulp is from farmed sustainable forests and
was produced with special regard for the environment.

Throughout, the printing and binding have been
planned to ensure a sturdy, attractive publication
which should give years of enjoyment.

If your copy fails to meet our high standards,
please inform us and we will gladly replace it.

INSIDE

Words & Music by Sting

© Copyright 2003 Magnetic Publishing Limited/EMI Music Publishing Limited.
All Rights Reserved. International Copyright Secured.

2. Love me like a father, love me like a prodigal son
   Love me like a sister, love me like the world has just begun.

3. Love me like a prodigy, love me like an idiot boy
   Love me like an innocent, love me like your favourite toy.

4. Love me like a virgin, love me like a courtesan
   Love me like a sinner, love me like a dying man.

5. Annihilate me, infiltrate me, incinerate me, accelerate me, mutilate me.

6. Inundate me, violate me, implicate me, vindicate me, devastate me.

7. Love me like a parasite, love me like a dying sun
   Love me like a criminal, love me like a man on the run.

8. Radiate me, subjugate me, incubate me, recreate me, demarcate me.

9. Educate me, punctuate me, evaluate me, conjugate me, impregnate me, designate me.

10. Humilate me, segregate me, opiate me, calibrate me, replicate me.

SEND YOUR LOVE

Words & Music by Sting

© Copyright 2003 Magnetic Publishing Limited/EMI Music Publishing Limited.
All Rights Reserved. International Copyright Secured.

1. In - side your mind is a re - lay sta - tion, a mis - sion probe in - to_ the un - know - ing.
2. There's no re - li - gion but sex and mu - sic, there's no re - li - gion but_ sound and danc - ing.

We send a seed to a dis - tant fu - ture then we can watch the ga - lax - ies grow - ing.
There's no re - li - gion but line and col - our, there's no re - li - gion but_ sa - cred trance.

This ain't no time for doubt - ing your pow - er, this ain't no time for hid - ing your care.
There's no re - li - gion but the end - less o - cean, there's no re - li - gion but the moon and stars.

Oh, send your love.

Send your love.

There's no re-li-gion but sex and mu - sic, there's no re-li-gion that's right or win - ning.

There's no re-li-gion in the path of ha-tred, ain't no prayer but the one I'm sing-ing.

Am7

Send your love.

Send your love.

WHENEVER I SAY YOUR NAME

Words & Music by Sting

© Copyright 2003 Magnetic Publishing Limited/EMI Music Publishing Limited.
All Rights Reserved. International Copyright Secured.

21

22

DEAD MAN'S ROPE

Words & Music by Sting

© Copyright 2003 Magnetic Publishing Limited/EMI Music Publishing Limited.
All Rights Reserved. International Copyright Secured.

Walk a - way from yes - ter - day,__ walk a - way__ to - mor - row.__

Walk a - way__ in ang - er, walk a - way__ in pain.__

Walk a - way__ from life__ it - self,__ walk in - to__ the rain.__

All this wand - 'ring has led__

me to___ this place.___ In - side the well of my mem-

-'ry, sweet rain of___ for - give - ness.

1.

I'm just hang - ing here__ in_____ space._____

2.

__ space._____

The shad - ows___ fall_____

a - round my_____ bed,___

when the hand___ of an an - gel,_____

Walk a - way_ from an - ger, walk a - way_ from pain._

Walk a - way_ from an - guish,

walk in - to_ the rain._

NEVER COMING HOME

Words & Music by Sting

1. Well, it's five___

© Copyright 2003 Magnetic Publishing Limited/EMI Music Publishing Limited.
All Rights Reserved. International Copyright Secured.

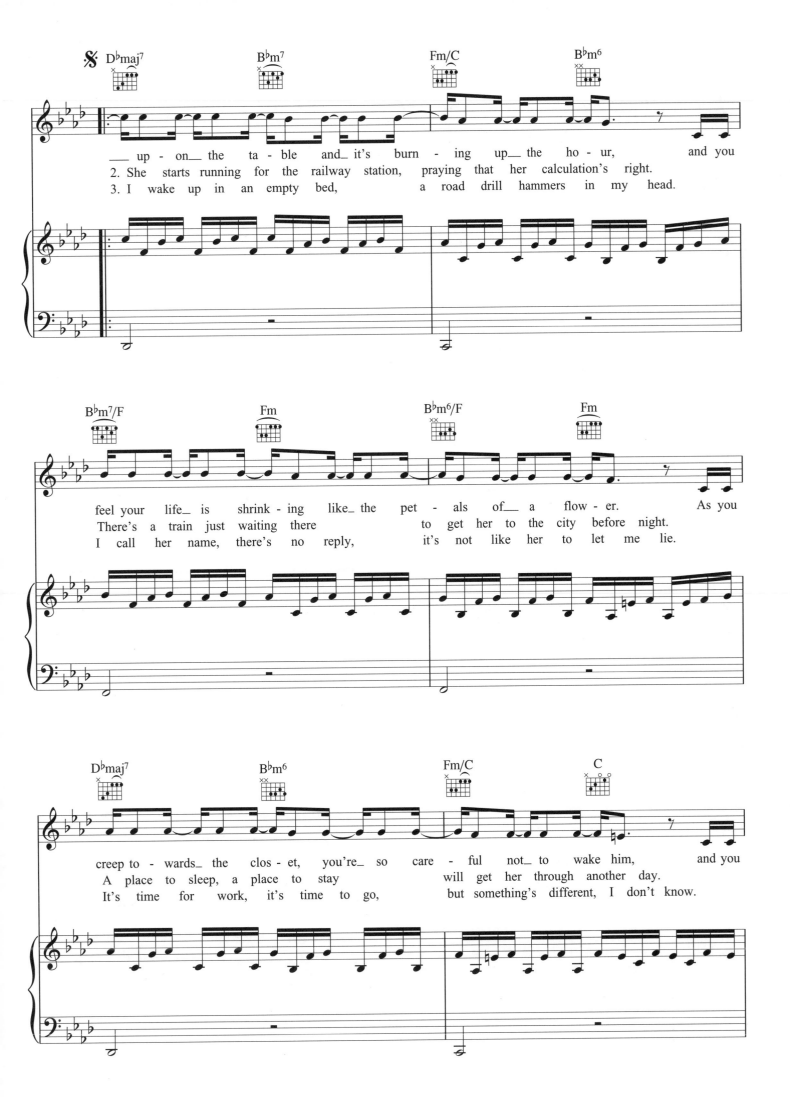

D.S. al Coda

Coda

Fsus⁴   Fm   Dm⁷ᵇ⁵   C/E

Well, she told him she was__ nev - er__ com - ing home.__

Fm/Aᵇ   Bᵇm   Bdim   C

44

STOLEN CAR

Words & Music by Sting

© Copyright 2003 Magnetic Publishing Limited/EMI Music Publishing Limited.
All Rights Reserved. International Copyright Secured.

kids just won't be qui - et as she runs a traf - fic light___ and she

Please take me danc - ing___ to - night,___ I've been all on___ my own.___
drives in - - - to the

___ You pro - mised one day___ we could___ 'swhat you said on___ the phone.___
night.

___ I'm just a pris - 'ner___ of love,___ al - ways hid from___ the light.___

E♭
Cm
3fr
F
Take me danc - ing,
please take me danc - ing to - night.
Esus2
2fr
So here am I in a
Csus2
3fr
Asus2
Gsus2
sto - len car at a traf - fic light,
they go from red to green,
G
Gm
3fr
A♭
4fr
B♭
Fm6add11
so I just drive in - to the

Repeat to fade

THIS WAR

Words & Music by Sting

1. You've got the mouth of a she - wolf in - side the
(2.) soul of in - dis - cre - tion, I was
(3.) dad - dy was a busi - ness - man, and it

© Copyright 2003 Magnetic Publishing Limited/EMI Music Publishing Limited.
All Rights Reserved. International Copyright Secured.

And you may win____ this war__ that's com-ing,__ but would you to-ler-ate the peace?__
Yes you may win____ this com-ing bat-tle,__ but could you to-ler-ate the peace?__

Ooh.____

In -

-vest-ing in mu-ni-tions__ and those lit-tle cot-ton flags; in-vest in

cot-ton flags;_ in-vest in wood-en cask-ets, in_ guns and bo-dy bags._____ You're in-vest-

-ed in op-pres-sion, in-vest-ing in cor-rupt-ion,_ in-vest in ev-'ry ty-ran-

-ny and the whole world's de-struc-tion._____

I i-

There's a war—

— on our de - mo - cra - cy,   a war on   our dis - sent.—   There's a war in - side re - li -
There's a war on Mother Nature,   a war upon the seas.   There's a war up - on the
There's a war on education,   a war on   information.   A war bet - ween the
A war   on our compassion, a war on   understanding.   A war on love and life

1-3.

- gion   and what Je - sus might have meant.—
forests, on the birds   and   the   bees.
sexes and every   nation.

4.

it - self.— It's war that they're de - mand - ing.—

63

FORGET ABOUT THE FUTURE

Words & Music by Sting

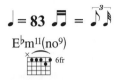

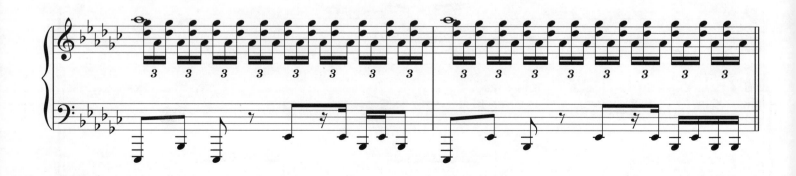

© Copyright 2003 Magnetic Publishing Limited/EMI Music Publishing Limited.
All Rights Reserved. International Copyright Secured.

I know we got some his - to - ry,__ we got some is - sues that we need to solve.__

But is it real - ly such a mys - te - ry?__ It's just the way that the world e - volves.__

Let me ask you your for - give - ness, ba - by; my heart is ev - er full of sor - row._____

We got to move in - to the fu - ture, may - be, and think a - bout a new to - mor - row._____

It's just__ too hard__ think-ing a-bout the fu - ture,__ so let's get on with the past.__

She said "We'd bet-ter check the ho-ro-scope, ho-ney,___

B♭7♯9

E♭m7

just in case this feel-ing was-n't meant to last.___

C♭maj7

It's just___ too hard_____ think-ing a-bout the fu-ture,___

so let's get on with the past."

How ma - ny times you ev - er hear me say_ I'm as flawed_ as a - ny oth - er hu - man be - ing?_

There sim - ply has to be a dif - fer - ent way,_ a whole_ new_ way of see - ing._

forget about the future,

and get on with the past."

THE BOOK OF MY LIFE

Words & Music by Sting

© Copyright 2003 Magnetic Publishing Limited/EMI Music Publishing Limited.
All Rights Reserved. International Copyright Secured.

no one_ can read   in_ the book of_ my   life._

There's a   chap - ter_ on fath - ers, a   chap - ter_ on sons._ There are pa - ges_ of con - flicts that no - bo - dy won,_ and the

78

bat- tles_ you lost,_____ and your bit- ter_ de- feat._ There's a page where_ we failed_ to meet._

_____ There are tales of_ good for - tune that could- n't_ be planned. There's a

chap- ter_ on God_ that I don't un- der- stand._ There's a pro- mise of Hea - ven and

Hell, but_ I'm damned if_ I see._

79

Though the pa - ges_ are num - bered, I can't

see where_ they lead For the end is_ a myst - 'ry

no one_ can read in_ the book of_ my_____ life._

N.C.

For the end is a myst - 'ry no one can read

in the book of my life.

Instrumental solo

SACRED LOVE

Words & Music by Sting

1. Take off those___ work - ing clothes,
2. Shut out the world be - hind___ us,
put on these high - heeled___
put on your long black

© Copyright 2003 Magnetic Publishing Limited/EMI Music Publishing Limited.
All Rights Reserved. International Copyright Secured.

I've___ been up, I've___ been down; I've been lone - some, in this

god - less town. You're my re - li - gion,___ you're___ my church; you're

the Ho - ly Grail at the end of my search.___ Have I been down on my knees___ for long___

don't love her, your best friend will. All the saints up in Hea - ven and the stars

up a - bove: it all comes down, it all comes down, it all

comes down to love.

(Take off your work - ing clothes, put on your long black

dress and your high-heeled shoes.)

I've been think-ing 'bout re-li-gion,___ I've been think-ing
think-ing 'bout the Bi-ble,___ I've been think-ing
think-ing 'bout the gar-den,___ I've been think-ing

'bout the things that we be-lieve.___
'bout A-dam___ and Eve.
'bout the tree of know-ledge and the tree of life.

I've been

I've been___ think-ing 'bout for-bid-den fruit,___ I've been think-ing 'bout a

man and his wife,___ yeah.

I've been think-ing 'bout,

SEND YOUR LOVE *Dave Audé Remix*

Words & Music by Sting

© Copyright 2003 Magnetic Publishing Limited/EMI Music Publishing Limited.
All Rights Reserved. International Copyright Secured.

LIKE A BEAUTIFUL SMILE

Words & Music by Sting

© Copyright 2003 Magnetic Publishing Limited/EMI Music Publishing Limited.
All Rights Reserved. International Copyright Secured.

that we walk all this while.

Like a beau - ti - ful dream,

it's just what it seems:_____ we're just float - ing up - stream_____

on E - ter - ni - ty's___ beam._____ So long as___ men___ can breathe or eyes